This edition published by Dempsey Parr 1999
Dempsey Parr is an imprint of Parragon

Parragon
Queen Street House, 4 Queen Street, Bath BA1 1HE, UK

2 4 6 8 10 9 7 5 3 1

Produced by Miles Kelly Publishing Ltd,
Unit 11, Bardfield Centre, Great Bardfield, Essex, CM7 4SL

Copyright © Parragon 1998

British Library Cataloguing-in-Publication Data
A catalogue record for this book is available from the British Library

Printed in Singapore

ISBN 1-84084-552-X

Editor: Margaret Berrill
Assistant Editors: Jenni Cozens, Lynne French, Louise Trott-Fenning
Design: Full Steam Ahead
Artwork commissioned by Branka Surla

Dedicated to
Mum, Butch, Dad and Jasmine
Paul and everyone at Parragon
My best friend Laura Stubbings
My family in Bristol
Nan and Grandad

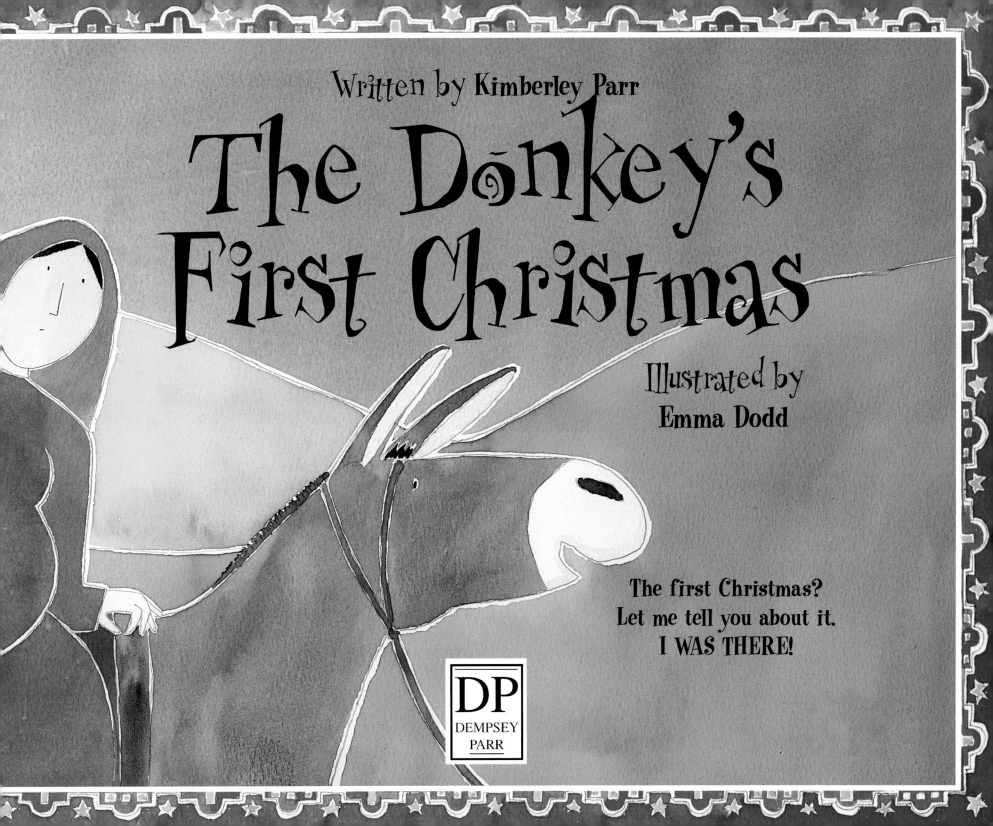

Written by Kimberley Parr

The Donkey's First Christmas

Illustrated by
Emma Dodd

The first Christmas?
Let me tell you about it.
I WAS THERE!

DP
DEMPSEY
PARR

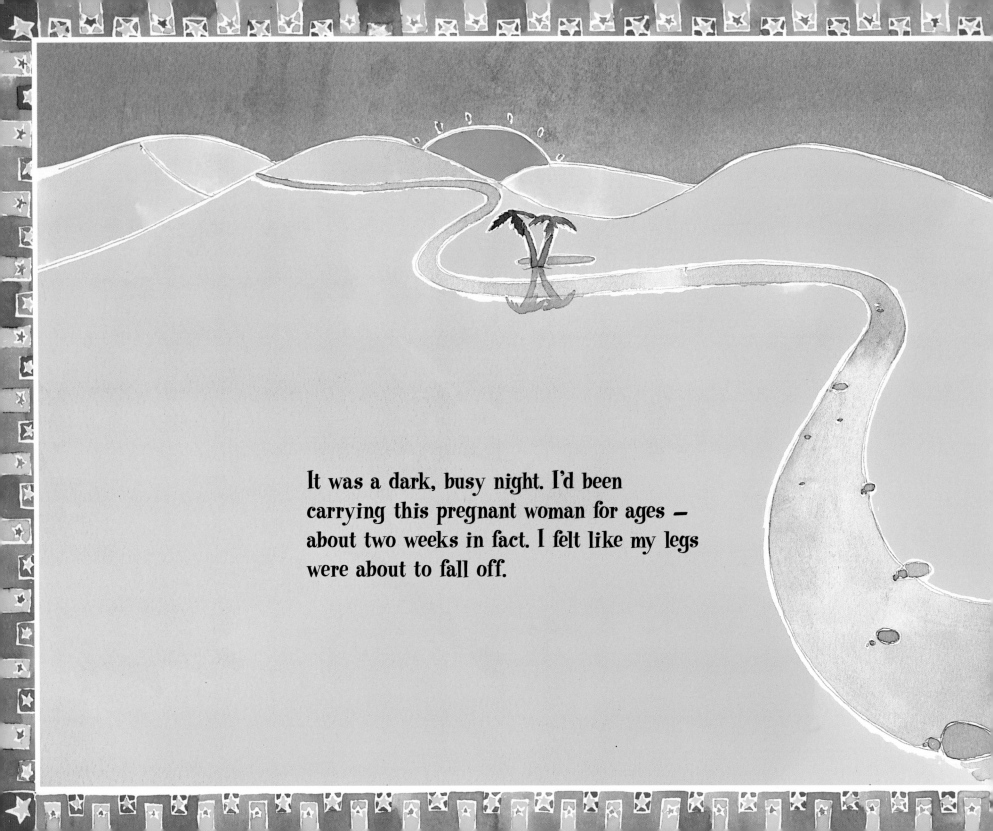

It was a dark, busy night. I'd been carrying this pregnant woman for ages — about two weeks in fact. I felt like my legs were about to fall off.

I was so thankful when we arrived in Bethlehem. I thought they'd get a room really quickly and I'd get a big stable with lots of hay. But I didn't!

My master, Joseph, spent about an hour looking for a room. When we got to the last inn, the innkeeper said,
"No space!"
I thought that was it. But Joseph begged and begged him and the innkeeper eventually gave in.

He showed us a little door that led to a musty old stable in the yard and left us to it.
So we all went in.

There was already a massive great big cow inside.

"They're NOT all coming in here, are they?" she said.

"I'm sorry. My mistress Mary is pregnant. We didn't mean to wake you up," I answered.

To that she replied,

"Still, it doesn't give you the right to come barging in here in the middle of the night and wake me up!"

And with that she turned her head
and wouldn't speak another word.

After a bit there was the sound of someone crying.

"They haven't got a baby in here, have they?" said the cow.

I looked up and saw a baby.

"Yes, it looks like it," I said, and we settled down to try to go to sleep.

A bit later I was woken by a knock at the door. Quiet, so quiet that you could hardly hear it.

"Come in," said Joseph softly.

There were three shepherds at the door.
I was a bit angry about this. Didn't
they understand? I wanted my sleep!

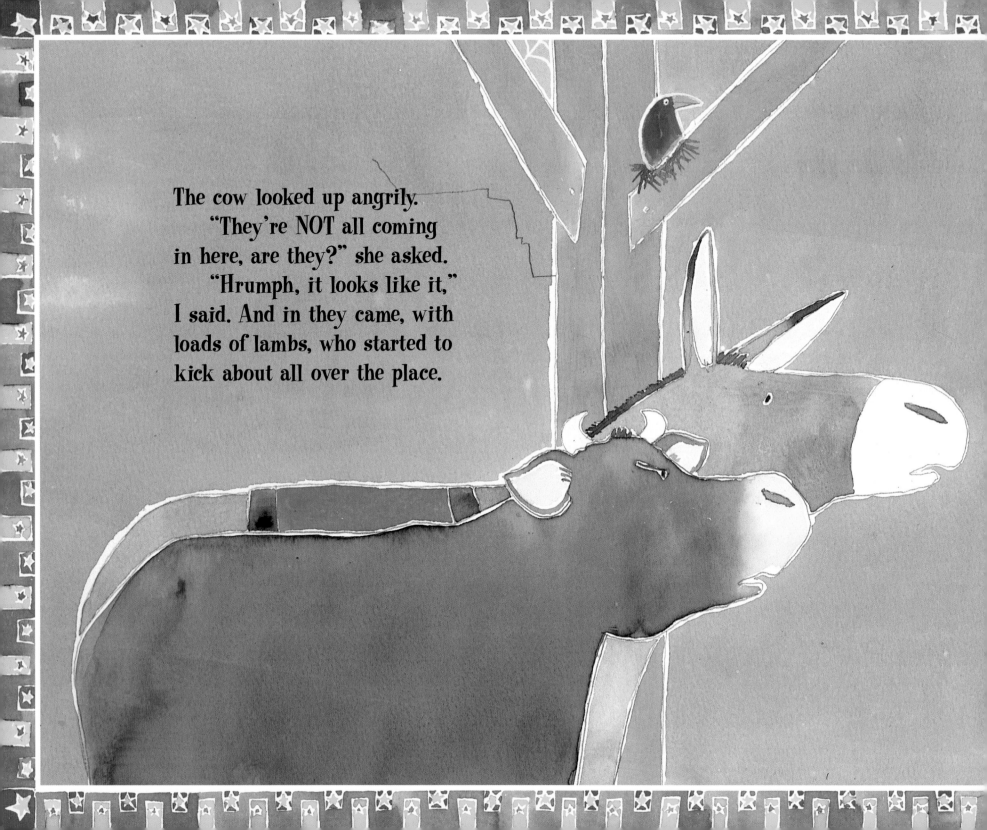

The cow looked up angrily.
"They're NOT all coming
in here, are they?" she asked.
"Hrumph, it looks like it,"
I said. And in they came, with
loads of lambs, who started to
kick about all over the place.

I asked them,
    "What are you doing here?"
And one of them said,
    "We have lowly gifts for the newborn king, Jesus. We have followed the bright star that hovers over your stable."

Then one of the shepherds grabbed a lamb and offered it to Joseph.

"For the little king," he said.

As soon as all of the shepherds had given lambs, they all sat around the manger, praying quietly.

And we settled down to try to go to sleep again!

KNOCK! KNOCK! KNOCK!

"Come in," said Joseph quietly.

The door opened and there were three kings. Yes, kings! I couldn't believe it.

"They're NOT all coming in here, are they?" asked the cow angrily.

"It looks like it," I said.

And in they came.

"We are kings from faraway lands. We have brought gifts for the baby, son of God, king of all the world."

"I have brought gold," said the first king. He walked
forward, stepping over the lambs, and knelt down next to
the manger. The others did the same, except that they said,

"I have frankincense," and "I've brought myrrh." Somehow
they found somewhere to kneel, and started praying too.
And we settled down to try to go to sleep.

Suddenly I heard faint singing of a chorus outside.
It was a crowd of angels. Hundreds of them.
"Can't a donkey have a decent night's sleep?" I muttered.
And the cow chipped in, "They're NOT all coming in here, are they?"

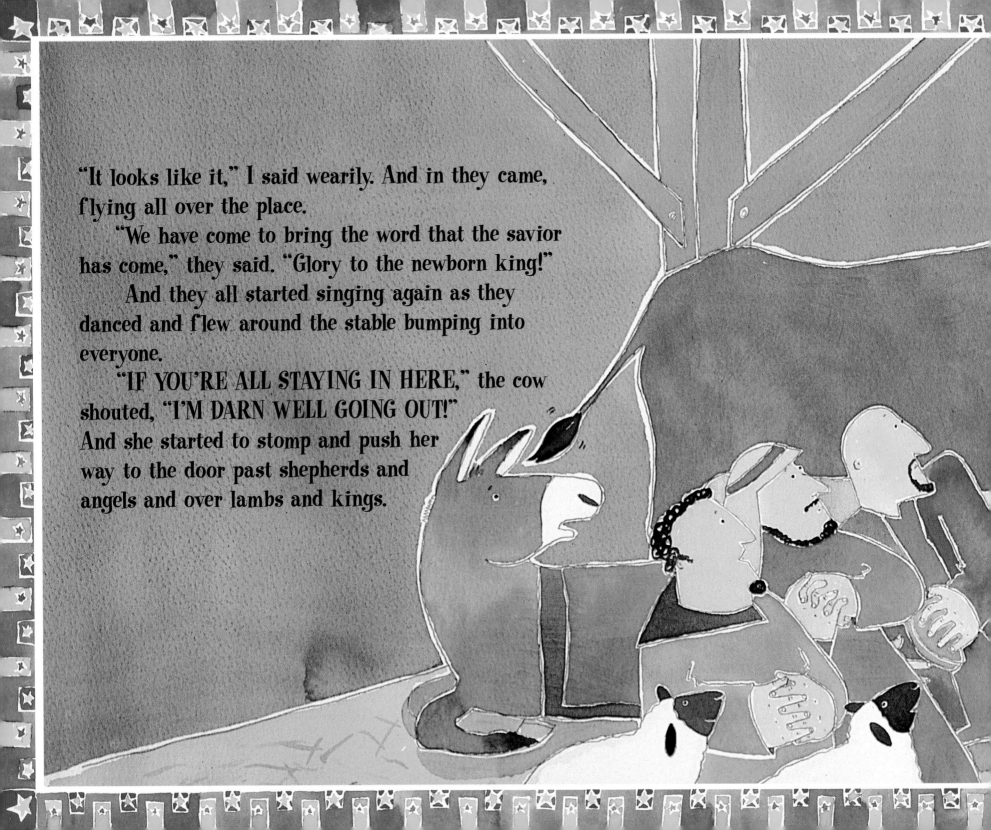

"It looks like it," I said wearily. And in they came, flying all over the place.

"We have come to bring the word that the savior has come," they said. "Glory to the newborn king!"

And they all started singing again as they danced and flew around the stable bumping into everyone.

"IF YOU'RE ALL STAYING IN HERE," the cow shouted, "I'M DARN WELL GOING OUT!" And she started to stomp and push her way to the door past shepherds and angels and over lambs and kings.

But a quiet voice whispered,
    "Would you like to see the baby?"
    It was Mary.
    "This is Jesus," she said, as she held him in the air.
    "Thank you for letting us all into your stable."
    The baby held up his little hand and touched the cow's nose
and the cow went all quiet and a bit pink and said softly,

"Oh, it's quite a big stable really. You're all VERY, VERY welcome."

I will never forget it. I WAS THERE!